ACTIVITES • CHARTS • USABLE TEMPLATE.

SEE IT. SAY IT. DO IT!

ORGANIZE IT!

WORKBOOK

Beth I. Fishman-McCaffrey, OTR, COVT • Patricia Dunnigan • Dr. Lynn F. Hellerstein

www.HiClearPublishing.com
Centennial, Colorado

Workbooks may be purchased for sales promotion and for volume pricing
by contacting the publisher:
HiClear Publishing, LLC, 7180 E Orchard Rd, #103, Centennial CO 80111
303-850-9499 • 303-850-7032 Fax • Info@HiClearPublishing.com

Cover Design, Interior Design and Illustrations by Annie Harmon
Interior Design layout assistance by Erika Gritters
Illustrations by Shannon Parish, Gene Willison and Erika Gritters

ISBN 978-0-9841779-3-6

1. Education.   2. Vision Therapy.   3. Parenting.
4. Organizational Skills.   5. Behavioral Optometry.
6. Success in Children.

Second Edition

Printed in the United States

Contents

Foreword

"I didn't have time to do my homework."
"My dog ate my notebook."
"I forgot my assignments."
"It took 2 hours to do my homework instead of 20 minutes!"
"I hate school!"

Do those comments sound familiar?

How is your child doing?

Does he have difficulty completing tasks?

Is she disorganized?

Does he use his assignment book?

Does her desk look like a disaster?

Does he forget where he puts his homework?

Is her room a mess?

Are you tired of fighting about homework?

Do you feel that your child may not be reaching his highest potential?

Does your child just "need" to apply himself?

Would you like to empower your child to develop his own easy and fun strategies for learning? How can you help your child before you drive yourself crazy?

See It. Say It. Do It! has been read by thousands of parents and teachers and has won numerous parenting and book awards. The *See It. Say It. Do It! Model* creates successful students and confident kids. It gives you a step-by-step process to help your child achieve his or her school goals—and life goals.

Schools use daily planners. The planners are sometimes helpful for organizing school assignments. However, the kids don't often use these planners other than when they are doing school assignments. They still have difficulty completing tasks and chores at home.

Two of my therapists at Hellerstein & Brenner Vision Center, P.C., occupational/vision therapist, Beth I. Fishman-McCaffrey, OTR, COVT and Early Childhood teacher/vision therapist, Pat Dunnigan, were frustrated with the difficulty that kids had in completing their home vision therapy activities. This pattern also extended to homework, family chores, and work completion in general. The kids always had great excuses why their work wasn't done. Bottom line—work completion was an issue.

Working with hundreds of students who were in vision therapy, Beth and Pat created organizational charts, utilized them with their patients, took their feedback, and modified the charts accordingly. They were able to finally create basic charts which kids successfully used—from primary grades through high school. In fact, many parents found that these charts worked so well they started using the charts for themselves.

Parenting is an awesome and very challenging responsibility. This is your opportunity to explore and create possibilities for yourself. Take a few moments just for you; relax, breathe and visualize yourself as a great parent—one who has the love, wisdom, strength, power and compassion to provide for your child.

These charts are much more than "to do" lists. If kids do not buy into the importance of the task, or take the responsibility to do the task, then the end result is often avoidance, distractibility, or they just don't do it.

The charts are carefully designed to implement the entire *See It. Say It. Do It!* process . . . Visualize, Declare, Take Action, **Ta-Dah!** It's done!

Boys and girls can benefit equally from these strategies. For simplicity, the pronouns, "he" and "she" are used interchangeably throughout the workbook.

Imagine your children having powerful tools to:

- Help them learn efficiently

- Read and write for fun

- Effectively prepare for tests

- Grow and blossom

You will be giving them a gift for life! *See It. Say It. Do It! Organize It!* will transform you and your child!

With Gratitude and Compassion,
    Lynn Fishman Hellerstein, O.D., FCOVD, FAAO

See It. Say It. Do It! Model

This workbook is based on the *See It. Say It. Do It! Model*. A quick review of the *See It. Say It. Do It!* process is included here. For a more detailed explanation of the process, refer to Dr. Lynn F. Hellerstein's *See It. Say It. Do It!: The Parent's & Teacher's Action Guide to Creating Successful Students & Confident Kids*. (HiClear Publishing, LLC, 2010)

See It!

See It!, or *visualization*, is the first step of the *See It. Say It. Do It! Model*. The word, *visualization*, conjures up many images and meanings for people.

Visualization is defined in numerous ways, depending on the person, the type of discussion and situation. For example, *visualization* may be simply defined as utilizing visual mental imagery or picturing in your "mind's eye."

Or the term *visualization* may refer to a more multi-sensory inclusive term utilizing sight, auditory, touch, smell and taste imagery as well as body sensations.

Visualization is the "knowing," the "I got it," or "gut feeling," through the orchestration of your senses.

Visualization definition:

The ability to imagine, sense, become aware of, move, manipulate and expand the pictures in your "mind's eye" and the feelings or senses in your body, thereby developing new perspectives and creativity.

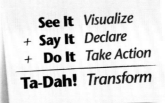

See It *Visualize*
+ **Say It** *Declare*
+ **Do It** *Take Action*

Ta-Dah! *Transform*

Say It!

Say It! is the second component of the *See It. Say It. Do It! Model.* It means to say out loud what you want to happen; and say it like it already has come true. In other words, start with the end result and then work backward. Declarations, also called affirmations, are important elements of the *See It. Say It. Do It! Model* that lead to transformation (**Ta-Dah!**). It is crucial to clearly and persuasively state the declaration of your vision. A strong declaration transforms your attitudes and expectations in life. How does this relate to kids? Easy—kids say what they are going to do or not going to do.

Fears

Does your child have great ideas, dreams and visualizations, but sits on the sidelines waiting for everything to be just right or fearful that he may fail at the task? He states, "It's not the right time," or "Maybe later," as his excuse. Have you ever heard those types of comments? Have you ever responded, "Just try it" or "Just do it"?

Everyone has fears, some so significant that they stop you in your tracks; some so minor that you laugh at them when you think back; and some more of a challenge. What are your fears? Heights? Failure? Making a mistake? Looking stupid? Not being good enough? Not having friends? Not being loved?

Are you able to manage your fears, or do your fears manage you? Remember, children have fears too. Fear can stop your child from taking action. He may be afraid to go out for a sport because he's not very coordinated. She may avoid raising her hand in class because of the fear of looking stupid and being laughed at. Watch how your child functions in these types of situations.

If your child makes a declaration, but does so in a very uninspiring way, the declaration will not be effective. However, when he makes a declaration that is clear, firm and strong and includes powerful body language, it will move and even encourage him. Your reply should be, "Say it like you really mean it!"

Do It!

Do It! is the third component of the *See It. Say It. Do It! Model*.

Successful businesses utilize action plans for their projects. You have probably created a form of an action plan recently. Do you make a "To Do" list—items that you need to pick up at the store, etc.? A list is certainly not a detailed action plan, yet it does note things that need to be completed. The important part of the **Do It!** section is to first make a strong declaration and then come up with the actions to make the project happen.

What happens when the *See It. Say It. Do It! Model* isn't utilized consistently or thoroughly?

These equations demonstrate what happens when all the steps of the *See It. Say It. Do It! Model* are not completed.

See It – Say It – Do It = DREAMER

Visualization without making a declaration or action plan usually results in a "dreamer" who has not realized his dreams. Do you know a teenager who has always talked about going to college, but just doesn't put in the effort to make good grades? He may have the dream of going to college but either never makes a strong declaration or takes no action. Excuses are abundant and not much is accomplished. Frustration and/or avoidance of tasks usually increase.

What about the child who works hard just to complete his work, but does not have a special interest, direction or goal? The equation would look like this:

Do It – See It – Say It = BUSY WORKER

Here is a child who just keeps working hard, with no particular direction, just spinning his wheels. Look at the workers who go to work daily, perform the same tedious duties, and then leave work at the end of the day. For some, this may be fulfilling; for others, they may be missing a real passion.

Fear often keeps a person from having the courage to follow his or her dreams.

Organized or Disorganized?

Some kids are naturally well organized in all areas of their lives, and some are disorganized. The goal is to find an organizational system that allows your child to **Do It!**—take action. It's a great habit to start, as it builds a lifetime of organizational skills.

There are many reasons why your child may be disorganized. The more common reasons include:

1. Learning Problems or Learning Disorders; these include difficulties with attention, sequencing, memory, visual and/or auditory processing.

2. Sensory Processing Disorder.

3. Not having a system to manage materials.

4. Amount of materials needed for each subject at school. Kids have multiple classes and each class requires a notebook and book. It's no wonder some kids never get their assignments done or turned in if they have to go through so many folders to find the papers they need.

5. Having too much stuff-creating a cluttered work area, backpack or locker.

6. Lack of responsibility, interest or motivation.

No matter what your child's preferred learning style is, some type of system needs to be used to help your child keep organized. The more creative the system, the better chance it will be utilized by your child. You shouldn't create the system—remember, it's for your child, not you (at least directly). Interestingly, if you haven't noted your child's learning style, pay attention. It's going to surface in this process. Consistency in utilizing the organizational system is critical to his success. For more information on learning styles, refer to the first chapter in the book, *See It. Say It. Do It!*

The complexity of the organizer has to be adapted for the age of your child. Older kids now use computerized organizers. For young kids, toys, books, even parts of their closet may be a good starting point. For example, kids learn early on that shoes go on the floor, not in their drawers.

How about making a game of putting colors of shoes together or similar types of shoes together (sandals and flip flops are on one part of the closet floor—school and dress-up shoes are placed next to them)?

Once the materials and workspaces are organized, then you can help your child to organize their activities and schedule. This will assure a smoother, more effective completion of task.

For additional information on other ways to get organized see the Appendix.

Time Management

This is a subject that many kids and parent's alike, have difficulty dealing with. Are you good at estimating how much time you have for tasks? Do you find that you never have enough time to complete an activity? Do you seem to mess around and before you know it, time's up?

Kids are the same way. Setting how much time you need and staying within the time limits is an art. This kind of organization is not only important for school work, it is also important for chores and daily living activities like cleaning your room, setting the table, etc. Initially, kids think that a schedule means that there are restrictions and all they do is work! What they soon realize is, when a time schedule is implemented, there is actually more time to play and have fun.

How to Use This Workbook

This workbook is divided into four parts plus an appendix. Part 1 explains the importance of being organized and how the *See It. Say It. Do It! Model* will be used to help your child become more organized. Part 2 includes questionnaires to determine the strengths & weaknesses of your child's organizational abilities. Part 3 gives samples and step-by-step instructions on how to create an organizational chart. Part 4 provides organizational templates for you to use.

The Appendix includes additional tips, sensory-motor activities, sample contracts, sample declarations and testimonials from parents who implemented strategies from *See It. Say It. Do It! Organize It!*

Getting Organized

Your child needs to "own" her chart from the very beginning. It starts with her visualization (**See It!**), declaration (**Say It!**), and then the steps and methods to take action (**Do It!**). The more fun and creative this process becomes, the more likely your child will use and continue to stay with the plan. If your child becomes bored or stops working on his plan, then a modification to the process is needed. Go back to the original declaration and plan, and then identify where the organizational chart needs to go at this point.

Rewards for accomplishing steps in the organizational chart are important for most kids. The reward can often be as simple as a hug, compliment, sticker or a toy he can earn. Does this work? Absolutely! Even children with significant learning problems will respond to the use of an organizational chart.

Creating a chart is helpful when your child has difficulty with the sequencing of commands. He can either draw pictures or cut out pictures from magazines representing all the tasks he needs to do for a certain time. Have him arrange the pictures in the appropriate order. Make sure the pictures are fun, colorful and meaningful for him. Now you just have one command to give: "Go check your chart!"

The organizational chart is a very effective, simple system to keep kids on track and to self monitor. It builds responsibility, accountability, organization and success. If used consistently, it can become routine and habitual. Eventually, the chart may become unnecessary or different charts may be needed. The key is making it routine and consistent.

How you communicate with your child when implementing the charts is critical. This includes what words you use, your tone and inflection. If you become frustrated because your child doesn't "get it," consider changing your descriptors and modifying your language and tone. You may need to simplify the activity. Always work at a level where your child succeeds. Otherwise, one or both of you will end up frustrated or angry—and probably with a few tears.

Here We Go!

Discuss the importance of organization with your child. Let her find examples of when she was organized and discuss how things went. Then examples of when she wasn't organized; what happened? For example, when she turned in her homework, how did she feel? What about when she was punished because she didn't complete her homework. How did she feel then?

Now, take a few minutes to do a *visualization* with your child. Here's an example of a *visualization* you can do regarding homework completion. You can modify this *visualization* for other specific tasks or chores.

Activity
Get Your Homework Done

Purpose: Learn how to successfully complete homework.

Instructions to child:

Parent: Sit comfortably, eyes open or closed. Take a couple of big breaths.

(Pause)

Parent: Picture yourself in your mind. Imagine watching a movie of you getting your homework assignment in school.

Parent: Where are you sitting?

Child responds: _____ .

Parent: What are you wearing?

Child responds: _____ .

Parent: What's the room like?

Child responds: _____ .

Parent: Write down your assignment in your school planner.

Child responds: _____ .

Parent: Now see yourself getting ready to come home. What are all the supplies that you need for your homework tonight? Pack your backpack.

(Pause)

Child responds: _____ .

Parent: In your mind, imagine your favorite place to study.

Parent: How does your body feel? (Not just "fine." Give him time to explore and describe any sensations.)

Child responds: _____ .

Parent: What do you notice?

Child responds: _____ .

Parent: Is there anything in your picture you would like to change? If so, what is it?

Child responds: _____ .

Parent: What would you like to bring into your picture to make studying fun, relaxing, and successful?

continued on next page

Child responds: _____ .

Parent: Bring in your organization genius or super mind and let's make a new version of the movie—change whatever you'd like to be better organized and more successful.

(Pause)

Parent: Re-wind the movie and now run your new movie. Watch it.

(Pause)

Parent: What was different in this new movie?

Child responds: _____ .

Parent: Re-wind it again. Jump into it and experience living it.

Parent: Now, how does it look and feel in this new movie? (You might give him an example of looking stronger or feeling bigger. Allow your child to create his state of how he would like to be.)

Child responds: I am (strong, big, smart, or whatever he stated).

Parent: Great! Say it again, loud and clear. State it with feeling, like you really mean it.

Child responds: I am _____ ! (Show him how to use body language to illustrate the power of his words. For instance, raise your hands like you are a winner, or jump up and down and show how powerful you are.)

Parent: Awesome job!

Parent: Now, take out your school planner and look at your assignment. Use your new powerful way of doing your homework. Complete your assignment.

Parent: Go to your organizational chart and mark that you have completed your homework.

Now give yourself a compliment.

Great job! Ta-Dah!

Commonly Asked Questions

What is an organizational chart?

The samples in this workbook are organizational charts. Organizational charts can be referred to as chore charts, task charts, action plans, responsibility charts, planner sheets or similar names. Have your child pick a name to use, even if it is silly.

Who would benefit from these organizational charts?

You and your child! These charts are designed to organize a person's activities or day.

How long before you see a change in your child's organizational skills?

This depends. Some children show improvement immediately, just by implementing the system. Others take longer. Success depends on the consistency of using the charts. You play a critical role in the consistency.

The charts are reminders of the tasks that need to be completed daily. This eliminates the issue of trying to remember what needs to be done, while alleviating any arguing and stress to complete a task.

How long do you keep using a chart?

Charts should be used until tasks or chores are mastered independently without checking the chart or needing external reminders (parents, guardians or others giving verbal cues) for something to be finished.

What do you do when you have mastered a chart?

Create new charts for other tasks to be initiated. For example, your first chart might be focusing on morning routines. After that is mastered, an afternoon or evening chart could be started. Charts can be added for any new project at any time.

What if my child has difficulty using a chart?

Charts should be adapted to allow for success. If your child struggles with the charts, then try these suggestions:

- Decrease the number of items on the chart.

- Use pictures, especially for a non-reader, to decrease demands until some mastery has occurred.

- Increase incentives.

- Make it fun!

Questionnaires

Look at each questionnaire and find those that apply to your child. Complete relevant questionnaires to gain better insight into your child's organizational skills both at school and at home. Be very careful not to pass judgment on your child's comments. Don't give him answers or contradict his comments.

You may discuss your child's comments to build your child's awareness of the way she spends her time. Make sure your comments are clear and gentle. Just observe and note. This will make your child feel comfortable answering the questions with honesty and clarity. Building your child's awareness of his use of time and organizational skills is crucial before implementing organizational tools.

If you or your child answer "yes" to any of the questions on the questionnaires, the organizational charts will be beneficial in helping your child become more organized.

School-Homework Questionnaire | Home Organization Skills | Personal Time | Parent Questionnaire

School-Homework Questionnaire

Have your child complete this questionnaire with your assistance. Help him to read the questions and write the answers for him if necessary.

This questionnaire relates to organizational abilities at school and for homework.

Question	Yes	No	Not Sure	Comments
Is your desk, locker, notebook or backpack disorganized or messy?				
Do you use your locker? If not, why not?				
Do you have difficulty starting your homework?				
Do you get distracted while doing your homework?				
Do you watch TV, play games on your computer, or video games while doing your homework?				
Do you have difficulty getting back to your homework after being distracted?				
Do you forget your homework assignments?				

School-Homework Questionnaire *(continued)*

Question	Yes	No	Not Sure	Comments
Do you forget the instructions for your homework?				
Do you lose homework or class work, often forgetting to turn the assignments in because you cannot find them?				
Do you bring home the supplies that you need to do your homework?				
Do you currently use a planner or assignment sheet?				
Do you complete school projects on time independently?				

Keep projects manageable for everyone. If the project is too big, it probably won't get finished and frustrations will set in. Dividing a big project into smaller projects will make it attainable and the success will feel great! Example – cleaning out closets. Pick one closet at a time, or do clothing one day and toys the next.

Home Organizational Skills

This questionnaire relates to how well your child organizes his personal and home life.

Question	Yes	No	Not Sure	Comments
Do you leave your toys and clothes around the house?				
Do you often forget where you have left your things?				
Do you often wait until the last minute to complete an assignment or project?				
Do you have difficulty remembering to do chores without having to be reminded?				
Do you fully complete your chores?				
Do you complete your chores correctly?				
Do you forget your homework assignments?				
Do you forget the instructions for your homework?				

Personal Time

This questionnaire relates to how your child spends his free time.

Question	Yes	No	Comments
Do you watch TV? If so, how much?			
Do you play video or computer games? If so, how much?			
Do you get enough sleep? How much time do you sleep each night?			
Do you spend time outside? If so, how much?			
Do you spend time talking on the phone or texting? How often?			
Do you ever start something but don't complete it?			
Do you get distracted or pulled away from a chore or an activity? If so, how often?			
Do you spend time with friends outside of your school day?			

Parent Questionnaire

Now it's your turn!

Question	Yes	No	Comments
Does your child understand the homework directions?			
Do you as a parent understand your child's homework directions?			
Does your child have difficulty starting an assignment or project?			
Does your child remember homework assignments?			
Does your child become distracted during activities or are they able to stay with the task until it is completed?			
Does your child do sloppy work?			
Does your child wait until the last minute to do an assignment or project?			
Does your child remember to hand in completed assignments?			

Parent Questionnaire *(continued)*

Question	Yes	No	Comments
Is your child organized—bedroom, locker, desk, backpack, notebooks?			
Does your child leave objects at school or home?			
Does your child misplace things and not remember where they are?			
Does your child make careless mistakes?			
Does your child act impulsively in situations?			

See if your answers on the parent's questionnaire are similar to your child's answers. If they are, you are ready to move onto the organizational charts. If they differ greatly, then you and your child need to discuss the differences. You may need to time his activities so that you both can really become aware of how much time he spends watching TV or doing his homework.

These questionnaires will guide you in creating your charts. This will ultimately help your child, as well as yourself, become more organized in all aspects of life.

Part

3

Sample Organizational Charts

This section contains sample organizational charts. These charts include typical activities most kids do in the morning, evening, and at school. Your child's chart should be individualized to meet his daily organizational requirements.

Help your child arrange the order of the activities. This teaches him how to prioritize. Don't overload the charts. Start with a few activities. Once he succeeds, then add more activities.

Have your child imagine the goals or chores when they are completed. Create a declaration of how he feels when he has successfully completed the goals. Now, start from the end result and create a list of things that need to be done. For example, if he needs to complete his homework, have him visualize (**See It!**) his homework completed and in his backpack.

Next, have him make a declaration (**Say It!**). Have him write the declaration on the top of his chart. For example, "I am responsible." In the Appendix, you will find samples of affirmations, declarations or inspirational words that you may use to give your child a positive verbal *"pat on the back"* for a job well done. If your child is old enough, have him chose an inspirational word or phrase which will allow him to acknowledge his success.

You and your child can then go through the organizational chart and write the steps that need to be done to accomplish his goal (**Do It!**). The organizational chart might start with putting the homework in the backpack. The step before that is checking over the answers. Then, before that, doing problems 1-4 and so forth.

Each individual chart will be unique to that person. For example, take a look at the Sample Morning Daily Chart on page 24. Under the first column, "Goal," list the chores that need to be accomplished. In the next column, "I Achieved My Goal," have your child initial when he has completed that goal. Be creative and allow your child to mark it however he chooses. Initials, stickers, stamps all work well. The last column, "Pat on the Back," is for the parent/guardian and child to acknowledge his achievement. Put a word of encouragement in the space to show your child how proud you are of his accomplishment.

Laminate the chart and use a dry erase marker to mark the achieved goal and "pat on the back" areas. This allows you to re-use the chart. Another option, you can place the chart in a clear page protector sheet. You will be able to write on the page protector with a dry erase marker and still wipe it clean to be used for the next day. Page protectors can be purchased at an office supply store.

ORGANIZE IT! TIP

If your child completes her daily goals independently, have her place a sticker on a Monthly Progress Chart (see page 51) for acknowledgement for the day's successes. After two weeks of stickers, or whatever time you agree to ahead of time, reward your child's successes on meeting her goals. The reward does not need to be materialistic. A reward can be a fun activity: swimming, bike riding, a day-off from chores, making brownies with mom or dad. The list is endless.

Occasionally throughout the process of using organizational charts, it is nice to throw in a surprise reward (decided by the parent) unexpected to the child. This will help motivate and encourage your child to continue using her charts.

For pre-readers, your child may use a chart like the one on page 27. Use pictures, stickers, or *Organize It!* cards that have the corresponding word(s) or action(s). (See pages 71-76 for examples). This way your child can use the picture to guide her in the task. The word(s) will also help her to develop sight word vocabulary skills. List the pictures in order of importance or sequence. Your child will put a star, sticker or initials after finishing each task on the chart.

Some ways you could use pictures are:

1. Laminate a chart; put Velcro on the chart and on the back of the picture. Remove the picture once the task is completed, or the child can take a dry erase marker and mark the chart below the picture to show completion. This would require the chart to be a little larger in order to have space to mark below the picture.

2. Put a self sticking magnet on the back of each picture and keep them on the refrigerator. As your child completes the task, he can take the card off the refrigerator and put it in a specified place, ie. box, folder etc. for future use.

Sample cards can be found in the back of this workbook in the Appendix. You may use these cards by cutting them on the dotted line (helpful if your child assists). There are also blank cards for you or your child to personalize. This will allow you to add tasks that you may want your child to do that have not been mentioned in this workbook.

Is It Working?

Your child needs feedback as to how the organizational system is working. The chart will help your child see that her goals are being met. Once she masters her initial goals, then it is time to add new goals or responsibilities.

As time goes on, refrain from asking or checking to see if the actions were accomplished. This will allow your child to experience success independently.

If your child is not meeting the goals you've agreed upon, then ask yourself why is this not being accomplished? There are several possibilities:

- It is not important to your child.
  Discuss how to modify or create the importance of the task.

- It is too complicated or detailed.
  Decrease the demands to achieve success, then build from there.

- Your child needs a better motivation or reward.
  Ask your child what his favorite reward is.

SAMPLE MORNING DAILY CHART

NAME:
Jamie

DECLARATION: I am responsible

REWARD: Fun time at the playground

GOAL	I ACHIEVED MY GOAL (INITIALS OR STICKERS)	PAT ON THE BACK (FOR ACHIEVING MY GOAL)
Make bed	JM	Way to go!
Brush teeth	JM	Thumbs up
Wash face	JM	Awesome!
Shower or bath	☺	Good Job
Get dressed	☺	☺
Put pajamas away	☺	Well done
Comb hair	JM	Looking good
Eat breakfast	✓	☺
Clean up breakfast dishes	✓	☺

SAMPLE EVENING DAILY CHART

NAME: Abby

DECLARATION: I will do my chores.

REWARD: Game night on Friday!

GOAL	I ACHIEVED MY GOAL (INITIALS OR STICKERS)	PAT ON THE BACK (FOR ACHIEVING MY GOAL)
Homework	AC	Way to go!
Eat dinner	☺	Thumbs up
Clean up dinner dishes	✓	Thanks for helping
Shower or bath	AC	☺
Put clothes in hamper	AC	Great job
Comb hair	✓	☺
Brush teeth	✓	☺
Back pack, homework, shoes, jackets ready for school	AC	☺
Read a book	AC	Nice reading
Watch 30 minutes of television	AC	Enjoy
Lights out at 8:30	AC	Sweet Dreams

ORGANIZE IT!
TIP

Remember your household chores may be different than the ones listed above. Your child's chart should be relevant to your household.

NAME:
Alana

SAMPLE SCHOOL DAILY CHART

DECLARATION: I am a good student

REWARD: Sleepover with a friend

GOAL

GOAL	I ACHIEVED MY GOAL (INITIALS OR STICKERS)	PAT ON THE BACK (FOR ACHIEVING MY GOAL)
Homework list	AB	Proud of you
Due dates	AB	Excellent
Materials/supplies to complete assignments	AB	Good remembering
Backpacks with necessary items, books, worksheets	AB	Awesome job
Check red/yellow and green cards	AB	Thumbs up
Homework check-off list	AB	Good job
Chart or school planner for daily school work	AB	Good follow through
Chart for project	AB	Way to shine

ORGANIZE IT! TIP

Some children do not work well if there are too many activities listed. They become overwhelmed. Use a minimum amount of words and add more as they become successful.

Sample Daily and Monthly Chart

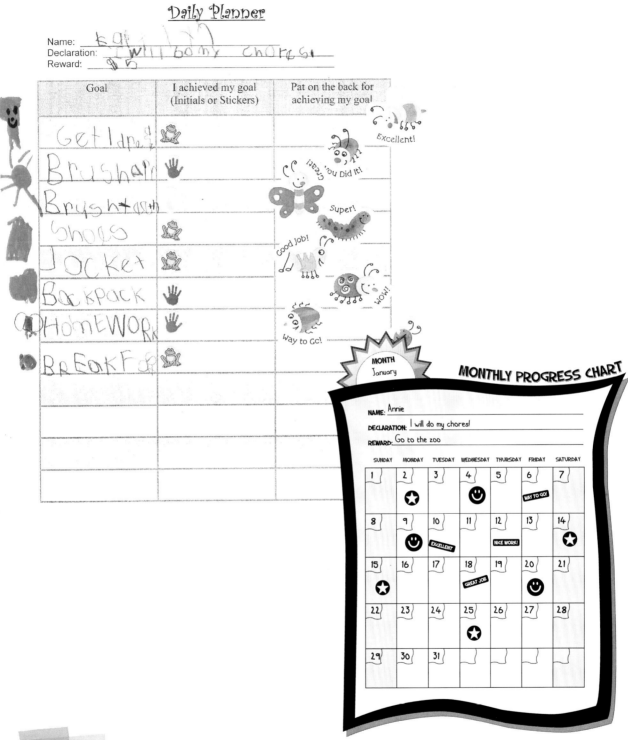

You might keep a monthly calendar so your child can see her daily successes and consistency.

Longer school assignments are challenging for children to keep focused on. Kids often procrastinate and put off the assignment until the last minute. Setting up an assignment chart can minimize stress. This increases the chances for success and completing the assignment in a timely manner.

When your child has completed the assigned tasks for the day, mark the assignment calendar to get an overall view of their progress.

Sample School Assignment Chart

Name: _Joey_

Declaration: _I am a great reader_

Assignment: _Book report_

Due Date: _24th_

Reward: _Play at the park_

Sun.	Mon.	Tues.	Wed.	Thurs.	Fri.	Sat.
5	6 Read Ch. 1 and 2	7	8	9 Read Ch. 3 and 4 Describe the setting	10	11
12	13 Read Ch. 5 Describe main characters	14	15 Field Trip	16 Read Ch. 6 and 7	17 No School	18
19	20 Read Ch. 8	21	22 Finish Book	23 Write a short summary about your book	24 Book report due	25

Ask your child's teacher to help you set up a schedule for homework and projects. This will allow your child to organize all of the pieces of the project. He will feel proud of each step on his way to accomplishing his goal. Be sure to "pat him on the back" each time he has completed a step.

Sample Organizational Chart for Adults

Name: *Beth*

Declaration: *I am a great parent*

Date: *June 24*

Reward: *Special dinner*

To Do Items	Due Date or Time	Completed	Comments
Take children to school	8:20	BF	Done
Drop off dry cleaning	8:30	BF	Done
Check inbox at work	9:00	BF	Completed
Proposal meeting	10:00	BF	Ready to go
Lunch meeting	12:30	BF	Wendy's Office
Take kids to sports	4:00	BF	Brad-soccer Shelley-volleyball
Pick up dry cleaning	Cleaner closes at 6:00	BF	By 5:30
School PTO meeting	7:00	BF	7:00 - 9:00

Organizational Chart for A Project: Painting Project

Name: *Pat*

Declaration: *I am an exceptional artist*

Date: *June 24*

Reward: *Manicure*

Steps for completion	Target date for completion	Date completed	Comments
Contacting painters for estimates	8/7	8/7	Got 3 estimates
Choose contractor	8/15	8/14	Decided and contacted contractor
Pick colors	8/12	8/12	
Set date for project to begin	8/15	8/14	
Move furniture	8/23	8/23	
Contractors arrive for project	8/24	8/24	
Estimated completion date	8/26	8/26	Manicure time!!

Part 4

Organizational Templates

These templates are samples for you to use.

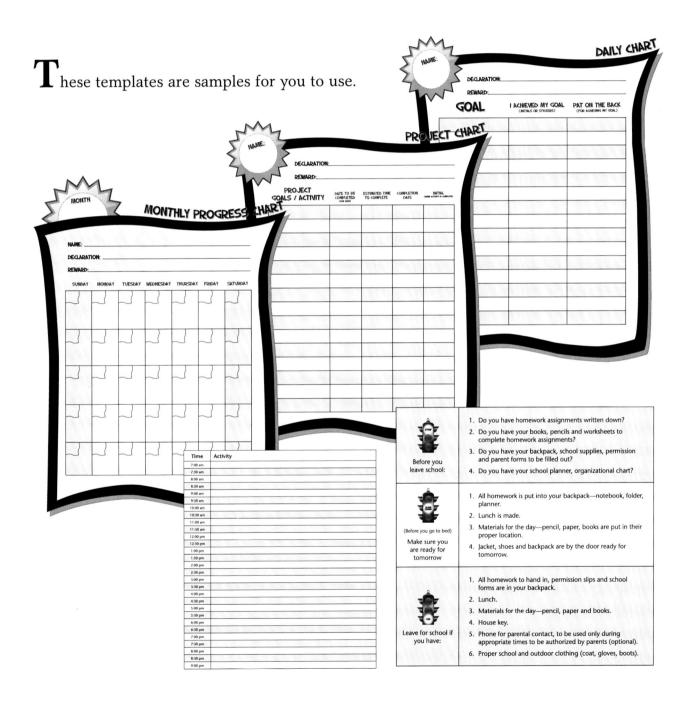

ORGANIZE IT!
TIP

Schedule a specific time during the week for organizing, like Saturday mornings at 10:00 a.m. for example. Take a little extra time to file papers which will clean up clutter and give the room a sense of order. You will feel good about how clean everything looks and extra happy when you need to retrieve one of those papers you filed down the road! This is also a good time to set up or use colored file folders. Blue for bills, green for house items, red for to do items, etc.

NAME:

DAILY CHART

DECLARATION:_____

REWARD: _____

GOAL	I ACHIEVED MY GOAL (INITIALS OR STICKERS)	PAT ON THE BACK (FOR ACHIEVING MY GOAL)

DAILY CHART

NAME:

DECLARATION:_____

REWARD: _____

GOAL	I ACHIEVED MY GOAL (INITIALS OR STICKERS)	PAT ON THE BACK (FOR ACHIEVING MY GOAL)

PROJECT CHART

NAME:

DECLARATION:_____

REWARD: _____

PROJECT GOALS / ACTIVITY	DATE TO BE COMPLETED (DUE DATE)	ESTIMATED TIME TO COMPLETE	COMPLETION DATE	INITIAL (WHEN ACTIVITY IS COMPLETE)

PROJECT CHART

NAME:

DECLARATION: _____

REWARD: _____

PROJECT GOALS / ACTIVITY	DATE TO BE COMPLETED (DUE DATE)	ESTIMATED TIME TO COMPLETE	COMPLETION DATE	INITIAL (WHEN ACTIVITY IS COMPLETE)

ORGANIZE IT!
TIP

If your child still has difficulty completing all tasks in an appropriate amount of time, try breaking the schedule into smaller time units. This gives him more structure with how many tasks he has, how long he has to complete a task, and how realistic his goals are. Figuring out the amount of time needed to complete a task is based on the individual child and needs to be adjusted accordingly. Try 15, 30 or 60 minute blocks of time. Once he successfully completes his goals in a timely manner, he has a better understanding of setting realistic goals. Then he can go back to a less structured daily planner.

Daily Schedule

Name: _____

Declaration: _____

Date: _____

Reward: _____

Time	Activity	Completed Goal	Pat on Back
7:00 am			
7:30 am			
8:00 am			
8:30 am			
9:00 am			
9:30 am			
10:00 am			
10:30 am			
11:00 am			
11:30 am			
12:00 pm			
12:30 pm			
1:00 pm			
1:30 pm			
2:00 pm			
2:30 pm			
3:00 pm			
3:30 pm			
4:00 pm			
4:30 pm			
5:00 pm			
5:30 pm			
6:00 pm			
6:30 pm			
7:00 pm			
7:30 pm			
8:00 pm			
8:30 pm			
9:00 pm			

Daily Schedule

Name: _____

Declaration: _____

Date: _____

Reward: _____

Time	Activity	Completed Goal	Pat on Back
7:00 am			
7:30 am			
8:00 am			
8:30 am			
9:00 am			
9:30 am			
10:00 am			
10:30 am			
11:00 am			
11:30 am			
12:00 pm			
12:30 pm			
1:00 pm			
1:30 pm			
2:00 pm			
2:30 pm			
3:00 pm			
3:30 pm			
4:00 pm			
4:30 pm			
5:00 pm			
5:30 pm			
6:00 pm			
6:30 pm			
7:00 pm			
7:30 pm			
8:00 pm			
8:30 pm			
9:00 pm			

Daily Schedule

Name: _____

Declaration: _____

Date: _____

Reward: _____

Time	Activity	Completed Goal	Pat on Back

Daily Schedule

Name: _____

Declaration: _____

Date: _____

Reward: _____

Time	Activity	Completed Goal	Pat on Back

MONTH

MONTHLY PROGRESS CHART

NAME: _____

DECLARATION: _____

REWARD: _____

SUNDAY	MONDAY	TUESDAY	WEDNESDAY	THURSDAY	FRIDAY	SATURDAY

MONTH

MONTHLY PROGRESS CHART

NAME: _____

DECLARATION: _____

REWARD: _____

SUNDAY	MONDAY	TUESDAY	WEDNESDAY	THURSDAY	FRIDAY	SATURDAY

Reminder Cards

These cards are to be used for visual cues like a traffic signal. Stop could be colored red; slow down for yellow; and green for go. The cards can be separated, laminated, and attached with binder rings to a backpack to give immediate reminders of tasks that need to be followed through with, either before going to school or leaving school. They are to be reviewed at nighttime for the next day's preparation. The colored reminders will help initiate independence and follow-through.

 Before you leave school:	1. Do you have homework assignments written down? 2. Do you have your books, pencils and worksheets to complete homework assignments? 3. Do you have your backpack, school supplies, permission and parent forms to be filled out? 4. Do you have your school planner, organizational chart?
 (Before you go to bed) **Make sure you are ready for tomorrow**	1. All homework is put into your backpack—notebook, folder, planner. 2. Lunch is made. 3. Materials for the day—pencil, paper, books are put in their proper location. 4. Jacket, shoes and backpack are by the door ready for tomorrow.
 Leave for school if you have:	1. All homework to hand in, permission slips and school forms are in your backpack. 2. Lunch. 3. Materials for the day—pencil, paper and books. 4. House key. 5. Phone for parental contact, to be used only during appropriate times to be authorized by parents (optional). 6. Proper school and outdoor clothing (coat, gloves, boots).

✂ Cut these cards out

Appendix

Tips for Success

1. Sure Ways to Complete Homework

- Establish a time and place for homework.

- Together, create a work space, free of distractions.

- Turn off the TV.

- Make an organizational chart. Commitment for follow-through for you and your child is important.

- Review Chapter 5 of the *See It. Say It. Do It!* book, for success stories on using organizational templates. Rewards based on chart results are often helpful.

- Remember, it is your child's homework, not yours.

- His job is to do the work and face the consequences if he fails to do what is expected. You need to determine ahead of time what the consequences will be if he does not do the work. No surprises!

2. Practice, Practice, Practice

- Practice visualizing at home or at school.

- Visualize using a lot of detail: color, size, shape, form. The more the detail, the more real the experience seems (**See It!**).

- Include other sensory systems like hearing, touching or feeling—even the smell of the surroundings.

- Include movement and motion (visualize doing the homework and turning it in).

- Go through specific action sequences.

- Envision alternatives—if you falter, how do you recover?

- Be aware of other things around you (the classroom, other kids).

- State your declaration loudly and clearly (**Say It!**).

- Practice frequently (**Do It!**).

- Breathe!

3. Get Results

- Spending the time now to become organized saves time in the long run.

- Be a role model. Be consistent with your planning and follow-through.

- If your child is struggling in school, maintain communication with your child's teacher. The teacher can help set up an organizational chart for class assignments and projects.

- Consider having him tested for learning difficulties.

- Make sure you have your child evaluated by a developmental optometrist. How do you find an optometrist who can provide a developmental vision examination? Ask your eye doctor these questions:

  - Do you do "near point testing?"

  - Do you give academically related vision testing?

  - Do you provide vision therapy or refer to someone who does?

  If your eye doctor is not clear or does not do this type of evaluation, then you can find a referral for a developmental optometrist at the "Locate a Doctor" section of the website: *www.COVD.org*.

Tips for Organizing Activities

This book primarily focuses on charts to help your child **See** what needs to be done and guide them to **Do** the activity so they can experience organizational success on an independent level. There are other areas of your child's life that needs to be organized and using a chart may not be the best solution.

Below are a few suggestions of ways to organize space and belongings. Each suggestion may take some time. However, the satisfaction of an organized room, home and a less stressful life will prove to be well worth it.

- ☑ Place a monthly calendar in a location where everyone in the family will **See It!** on a daily basis. Suggestion: put a magnet on the back of the calendar and hang it on the refrigerator or place it on the back of a door that everyone in the house uses to enter and leave. Put everything on the calendar that will be happening: sports activities, school activities, doctor appointments, meetings, family date/game night, etc. This will act as a reminder to everyone of what is going on and help keep the family organized.

- ☑ Organize a child's room by placing belongings/toys in containers with lids. This form of organizing can be started at a very young age by putting pictures of what goes in each container on the outside of the container. Obtain the pictures from the packages when you purchase the item, cutting them from a sales advertisement, or going on-line to search for a picture of the item.

- ☑ As your child becomes a reader start putting the words on the containers. This will allow her to read (**See It!**) what is in each container and help her learn how to clean up and put things in their proper place (**Do It!**). This also provides an easy way to rotate toys in and out of your child's room so that she does not become bored with items she has to play with.

- ☑ Organize your child's clothing by using a clothing organizer that separates clothing by the day.

- ☑ Prior to a holiday or child's birthday, sort through his containers. Have him choose toys he no longer plays with and donate the toys to charity. This will free up containers for new items coming into your child's life as well as teach him to share with others. Have him go to a donation center with you. It is never too early to teach your child about giving.

☑ Clean out you child's dresser drawers. Too many items make it difficult for her to put her clothing items away neatly. Pack up winter clothes during the summer and vice versa in the winter allowing for fewer items in the drawers. Small containers can be placed in drawers to hold items like socks and underwear.

Giving a specific place for each item of clothing will help your child **See** where things go. This helps him to learn to put things in their place instead of just throwing them into a drawer. Your child becomes responsible for his own belongings while developing skills to become more organized.

☑ Boxes of games and puzzles often break and individual pieces left lying around the house are lost. Suggestion for puzzles—buy one large container and label it puzzles. Place the puzzle pieces in large Ziplock bags with the top of the puzzle box (picture of the puzzle). The top of the puzzle box will allow the child to **See** what puzzle is in each ziplock bag and keep them neatly in one place. Each bag can be placed in the large plastic container for storage. The same can be done for games. Pieces will not be lost and everything will have a place that is neat and organized allowing for items to be easily found.

☑ On page 55, you will find sample reminder cards. They can be laminated and placed on your child's backpack. These will help her remember everything she needs to get ready for school, bring home from school or have packed for the next school day. This will allow her to see what needs to be done and help her follow through independently (**Do It!**).

☑ Write on a piece of cardstock paper or cut out pictures of everything your child needs for sports practice or games. Laminate the card and attach it to his sports bag. Your child will see the list prior to leaving the house for his practice or game. He will pack up his own sports bag (**Do It!**) and ensure that all items needed are available. This way your child will learn how to be responsible for his own needs and property.

☑ Help your child find the books and supplies she needs for class. Cover each book in a different color and then buy matching colored notebooks. Example: Geography book covered in green and the geography notebook is green; math book covered in red and a red notebook; etc.

☑ You can color code any of the child's belongings and materials, or, if you have several children, use color coding to mark each child's belongings or materials.

☑ To eliminate clutter, avoid impulse buying. For example, borrow a book from the library instead of buying a book. You will read it faster and won't keep a book around the house that you will most likely only read once. Plus, children love visits to the library!

- *When you purchase your containers, make sure that they have lids and are large enough to hold the items you plan on putting in them.*

- *Containers with lids make it easy to stack.*

- *Clear containers allow you to **See** what is in each container.*

- *Name tags with adhesive backs or adhesive mailing labels work well for labeling containers. Decide, with your child, what the label will say. This gives him his own cognitive set for remembering.*

- *A pocket photo album or a notebook with page protector sheets is a great way to organize pieces of paper that you want to have access to for repeated use. Organize recipes by categories – desserts, cakes, and pies, etc. Put cards in a pocket of a photo album for ease in locating. Leave open pockets so you can add new recipes as you go.*

- *Notebooks with page protectors are a great way of organizing receipts you need to keep handy.*

Benjamin Franklin once said, "A place for everything and everything in its place." This way of thinking makes for a happy, well functioning and organized person.

Sensory Motor Activities

Most children have difficulty sitting for long periods of time. Introducing a specific break time while your child is doing homework can often result in better concentration, focus and completion of tasks.

Kids naturally want to move. Encourage specific movements such as:

- Walking, running or skipping

- Carrying or moving heavier objects such as laundry baskets filled with clothes

- Dog shake (see page 48 in the book *See It. Say It. Do It!*)

- Stretching

More specific activities are available in Chapters 3 and 4 of the book *See It. Say It. Do It!*

Other recommendations that help kids stay focused are:

- Muscle massage

- Deep breathing for relaxation

- A good diet

- Adequate sleep

- Taking good care of her body

- Frequent laughter

- Having fun!

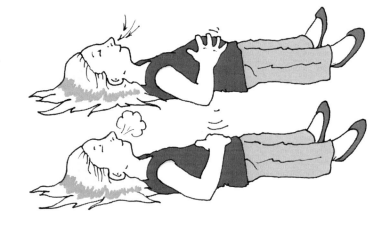

ORGANIZE IT!
TIP

A relaxed body and mind creates an optimal learning environment.

Contract

Many kids, as well as adults, have difficulty motivating themselves to stay on track and complete their goals. This is especially true with projects or tasks that they do not feel are that important. Your child should have input and help in designing the contract. A signature from each of you is essential. You are giving your word and need to stand behind what you have agreed to; just like you would expect from your child. Remember, you are the role model! This reminds your child that he is committed to the goal; it was not just you making him do it!

Contract:

I, _____ Freddie _____ have made an agreement with _____ Mom and Dad _____

        child   parent/guardian

to take the responsibility of completing my weekly chores by Friday afternoon.

Freddie

_____
Child Signature

_____
Parent Signature

This contract is a sample and can be modified to be specific to your needs. It can include more than one responsibility or be more specific on what is expected and agreed upon.

ORGANIZE IT!
TIP

At the end of the evening take 5 minutes to pick up everything that is not in its place and put it in a basket. When you have extra time, have everyone in the house retrieve their belongings and put them where they belong. If you need to find something before the items get put back where they belong, you will only need to look in the basket instead of every room in the house.

If a task will only take a few minutes to complete, do it immediately.

Contract

Date: _____

I, _____

have made an agreement with

_____

to take the responsibility of completing

_____

_____

_____

_____

by _____.

_____   _____

Child Signature   **Parent Signature**

Declarations

I am perfect, just as I am.	I am a great student.
I am powerful	I love to have fun.
I love to laugh.	I am loved.
I am strong.	I am happy.
I am responsible.	I am a neat kid.
I am special.	I belong.
I shine like a star.	My thoughts are powerful.
I believe all things are possible.	I care about other people.
I love who I am.	I can do anything.
I believe in myself.	I am generous.
I am confident.	I am kind.
I am patient.	I am smart.
I look for the good in all situations.	I am talented.

ORGANIZE IT! TIP

Always set a goal. Be realistic so what ever your goal is it can be accomplished. A declaration statement should always be made. It gives you ownership over what your goal is. Don't forget to have everyone, child or adult, make a declaration statement.

Inspirational Words and Phrases

Faith	Love
Peace	Hope
Give	Joy
Magic	Dream
Listen	Smile
Caring	Think
Share	Laugh
Believe	Wonder
Dare to try	Attitude
Winners make the grade	The journey is the prize
Trust	Believe you can
Shine	Great things are worth the work
Confidence	If you think you can—you can
Respect	Never settle for less than your best
Free	Keep on smiling
Beauty	The time is always right
Be you	Never, never quit
Way to go	You are responsible for your own actions
Thumbs up	You never know what you can do until you try
Great job	
Nice work	

Always reward yourself or the individual that is following through on a task after the work has been done.

Testimonials

Since we implemented the organizational charts, the emotion and drama surrounding the morning routine, getting homework done and the bedtime routines have significantly decreased. Because our daughter understands she is responsible for accomplishing her tasks and knows what is expected of her, we, as parents, do not need to continuously nag her to complete her routine tasks. Thanks to the organizational charts, we have more peace in our household.

—Heidi H.

Parent

I can't give enough accolades for the organizational charts. They have made our lives so much better at home. No more arguing and having to deal with meltdowns. Our son is thriving with the structure and is now taking pride in initiating getting dressed, brushing teeth, etc. We all needed this and our home feels much happier!

—Wendy C.

Parent

One of my students recently had a psych-ed evaluation and, on of the recommendations, was to use a scheduling sheet at home. I gave the parents one of the organizational charts from Beth. They were amazed at the immediate changes they experienced with their son. He became more independent without the parents having to continually nag him in the morning. Our hope is that this organizational chart will become ingrained into his mental processes. While these organizational charts are beneficial for students with unique learning profiles, they can benefit anyone who needs some organization strategies. They also help children who need to build their independence with regards to daily activities. Honestly, what child doesn't need help in these two areas?

—Katie P.

Learning Specialist

Beth introduced Jackie and me to organizational charts several weeks into the school year. Prior to that time we were experiencing a lot of confusion on assignments due and missing homework assignments. Now Jackie has a starting point written down on the organizational chart so she is spending less time trying to get organized. The routine organizational chart is helpful for morning and evening routines. With the reinforcement of a planner, distractions are kept to a minimum. Thank the heavens for Beth and organizational charts.

—Maureen W.

Parent

We have seen a complete 180 in Evan's willingness to try to do her morning routine on her own since using an organizational chart. Her attitude is more positive and she is now trying new chores as part of her routine. We are very impressed and quite frankly surprised at her abilities and capabilities with using the chart.

—Cathy H.
Parent

The organizational chart has been a great tool for us to have. Although the transition of using a goal chart does take some commitment and patience from both the child and the parent, having an efficient day and night routine without the hassles or struggles that usually occur has been a wonderful benefit. Our son has demonstrated improved organization and time management skills and is now independent in his daily routine. This experience for all of our family has been very rewarding.

—Jill J.
Parent

We have hung a calendar in the bathroom to help remember tasks or appointments before leaving the house for the day. It works wonderfully. My daughter has now adopted the calendar in the bathroom to keep her schedules organized and she hasn't missed a beat. Thanks for sharing See It. Say It. Do It! organizational workbook—my next step to organizing our lives.

—Sherry M.
Administrative/Professional Faculty Member

This workbook provides many helpful steps in optimizing organization for our children. The utilization of the basic components listed here involving executive functioning, allows children the structure and consistency needed for personal as well as academic success. These authors have anticipated the skills necessary for students to be able to follow through with classroom assignments or to simply complete the tasks asked of them within the home environment. This valuable tool also incorporates the value of visualization and how that can help move students from a negative self-perception to one that is positive and productive. I highly recommend this tool for parents as well as for those working in the field of education.

—Vicki Nilles, Ph.D. Candidate
Assistant professor of teacher education at Metropolitan State College,
Educational Consultant, Parent

ORGANIZE IT! CARDS

Cut these cards out ✂

EAT BREAKFAST

PUT CLOTHES IN HAMPER

CLEAR DISHES

MAKE BED

READ 15 MINUTES

GET SCHOOL STUFF READY

PUT SHOES AND SOCKS ON

SET THE TABLE

HELP WITH DINNER

ORGANIZE IT! CARDS

Cut these cards out

DO YOUR HOMEWORK

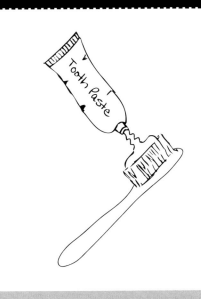

BRUSH YOUR TEETH

TAKE A SHOWER/BATH

EMPTY THE DISHWASHER

FEED THE PET

BRUSH YOUR HAIR

GET DRESSED

READ 15 MINUTES

CLEAN YOUR ROOM

Create your own cards. Have Fun! ✂ Cut these cards out

Conclusion

As a parent, you become the CEO—Chief Encouraging Officer. An important parental duty is to encourage your child to create big dreams. Talk about them frequently. Assist him in finding a way to move toward his dreams.

As described in the book *See It. Say It. Do It!*, your child's confidence increases with the success he feels at home and at school. That success is rooted in his ability to learn how to look within and become aware of all the possibilities he can achieve.

He learns that he can take charge of his thoughts, visualizations, declarations and actions in all areas of his life. He becomes more confident and has strategies when he needs them to overcome barriers and obstacles. He becomes more successful in school and more interested in the joy of learning. It's the **Ta-Dah!** . . . the "I did it!"

Teach your son or daughter to be a lifetime learner. Know that you are the role model for your children. Take a risk yourself! Use the *See It. Say It. Do It! Model* to guide you to guide your child. When you walk your talk, it is so much easier for your child to follow in your footsteps. Have fun!

About the Authors

Beth I. Fishman-McCaffrey, O.T.R., C.O.V.T., *Registered Occupational Therapist*

Beth is a pioneer in integrating Sensory Integration Therapy with Optometric Vision Therapy. She has been in a private occupational therapy practice for over 20 years working with patients of all ages, abilities and disabilities. Her expertise and therapeutic knowledge has impacted hundreds of patients by improving their functional skills which in turn enhances their lives.

Beth received her Bachelor of Science degree in occupational therapy from Colorado State University. She has worked in a variety of settings, which include a private optometric practice, a private occupational therapy practice, group homes, and the public school system. Beth has a certification in the identification and treatment of children with sensory processing disorder. She lectures and consults with educational, rehabilitative and many other groups on identification and treatment of children with sensory motor difficulties. In addition, she consults with patients with mild to moderate brain injuries.

She holds a certification as an optometric vision therapist (COVT), and a certification in Educational Kinesiology (a holistic approach to helping the body to identify stressors, organize, enhance and increase learning potential). In addition, she holds a certification as a provider for the Advanced Brain Technologies Listening Program with Bone Conduction. Beth served on the board of the Occupational Therapy Association of Colorado from 1996-1998 as the educational/conference chairperson.

Patricia A. Dunnigan, *Educator, Vision Therapist*

Pat Dunnigan has served as an educator for 25 years. She has worked in both the public and private sectors with kindergarten-aged children, which is her area of expertise.

Pat is the creator of a revolutionary experiential enrichment program that is delivered in a public school setting. She loves what she does and the outcomes of "Pat's Kids" are remarkable.

Pat has also been a vision therapist for the past 6 years, working with patients of all ages. Using her teaching background, she helps children grow and reach their potential.

Dr. Lynn F. Hellerstein

Lynn F. Hellerstein, O.D., FCOVD, FAAO, has been a pioneer in vision therapy for more than 33 years. Her expertise and leadership in developmental optometry has inspired thousands to improve their vision and enhance their lives. She has successfully treated children and adults with learning, visual perception and visual motor difficulties. In addition, she consults with athletes to improve their sports performance.

Dr. Hellerstein has published extensively on vision related topics. Her award-winning book, *See It. Say It. Do It!: The Parent's & Teacher's Action Guide to Creating Successful Students & Confident Kids* (HiClear Publishing, LLC, 2010) is a remarkable resource for parents, educators and therapists.

Dr. Hellerstein is the founder of a private optometric practice in Centennial, CO (in Metro-Denver). She is a frequent lecturer and consultant to educational groups, sports teams, rehabilitation and other medical professionals. A Fellow of the College of Optometrists in Vision Development (COVD) and American Academy of Optometry, Dr. Hellerstein is a past-president of COVD. She is also an adjunct professor at several colleges of optometry throughout the United States.

To contact any of the authors about presentations or workshops, call or e-mail:
info@SeeItSayItDoIt.com
303-850-9499
www.SeeItSayItDoIt.com

To contact the authors about vision therapy:
info@HBVision.net
7180 E. Orchard Road, Suite 103
Centennial, CO 80111
303-850-9499
www.HBVision.net